CARL PHILIPP EMANUEL BACH

Miscellaneous Keyboard Sonatas,

1731 – 1744

Edited by Darrell M. Berg, Wolfgang Horn, and Mark W. Knoll

The Packard Humanities Institute

LOS ALTOS, CALIFORNIA

Carl Philipp Emanuel Bach: The Complete Works

CPEB:CW OFFPRINTS, NO. 101

This edition is based on series I, volumes 5.1, 6.1, and 6.2 of *Carl Philipp Emanuel Bach: The Complete Works*, an editorial and publishing project of The Packard Humanities Institute, in cooperation with the Bach-Archiv Leipzig, the Sächsische Akademie der Wissenschaften zu Leipzig, and Harvard University. The complete introductions to this edition are available online, along with performing material, at http://www.cpebach.org. Full scores with critical commentary are also available from the publisher.

A complete list of the published study scores may be found on our website:
https://cpebach.org/offprints.html

CONTENTS

LIST OF FIGURES

RACCOLTA
DELLE
PIÙ NUOVE COMPOSIZIONI
DI CLAVICEMBALO
DI DIFFERENTI MAESTRI ED AUTORI.
PER L'ANNO 1756.
FATTA STAMPARE
DAL
Sgr. FEDER. GUIGLIELMO MARPURG.

LIPSIA
Preſſo GIO. GOTTL. IMAN. BREITKOPF.

FIGURE 1. Title page from Marpurg's *Raccolta delle più nuove composizioni*.
Brussels, Conservatoire Royal de Musique, Bibliothèque.
Koninklijk Conservatorium, Bibliotheek, 6307

Sonata in B-flat Major

Wq 62/1

Presto

Allegro assai

FIGURE 2. Wq 65/1, mvt. i, mm. 1–30, in the hand of Anon. 303.
Staatsbibliothek zu Berlin—Preußischer Kulturbesitz, Musikabteilung mit Mendelssohn-Archiv,
Mus. ms. Bach P 775, p. 87

Sonata in F Major

Presto

Sonata in A Minor

Wq 65/2

Sonata in D Minor

Wq 65/3

Allegro di molto

26

28

Sonatina in F Major

Wq 64/1

Sonatina in F Major

Wq 64/1 (early version)

38

Sonatina in G Major

Wq 64/2

Allegro

Sonatina in G Major

Wq 64/2 (early version)

48

Sonatina in A Minor

Wq 64/3

Sonatina in A Minor

Wq 64/3 (early version)

58

Sonatina in E Minor

Wq 64/4

Sonatina in E Minor

Wq 64/4 (early version)

Allegretto

Sonatina in D Major

Wq 64/5

Allegro ma non troppo

Sonatina in D Major

Wq 64/5 (early version)

Allegro ma non troppo

Sonatina in C Minor

Wq 64/6

Allegretto

Sonatina in C Minor

Wq 64/6 (early version)

Sonata in E Minor

Wq 65/5

Allegro di molto

Sonata in E Minor

Wq 65/5 (early version)

Sonata in G Major

Wq 65/6

Adagio di molto

Sonata in G Major

Un poco allegro

Wq 65/6 (intermediate version)

Adagio molto

Sonata in G Major

Wq 65/6 (early version)

Sonata in E-flat Major

Wq 65/7

Allegro moderato

Sonata in E-flat Major

Wq 65/7 (early version)

Sonata in C Major

Wq 65/8

Sonata in B-flat Major

Wq 65/9

Sonata in A Major

Wq 65/10

Sonata in A Major

Wq 65/10 (revised early version)

142

Sonata in G Major

Wq 62/2

*autograph cadenza from A:

Cantabile

Sonata in G Minor

Wq 65/11

Allegretto grazioso

FIGURE 3. Title page of Marpurg's *Clavierstücke mit einem practischen Unterricht*.
Washington, Library of Congress, MT 243 .M23 (Case)

Sonata in D Major

Wq 62/3

Andante

Sonata in D Major

Wq 62/3, earlier version

Siciliano

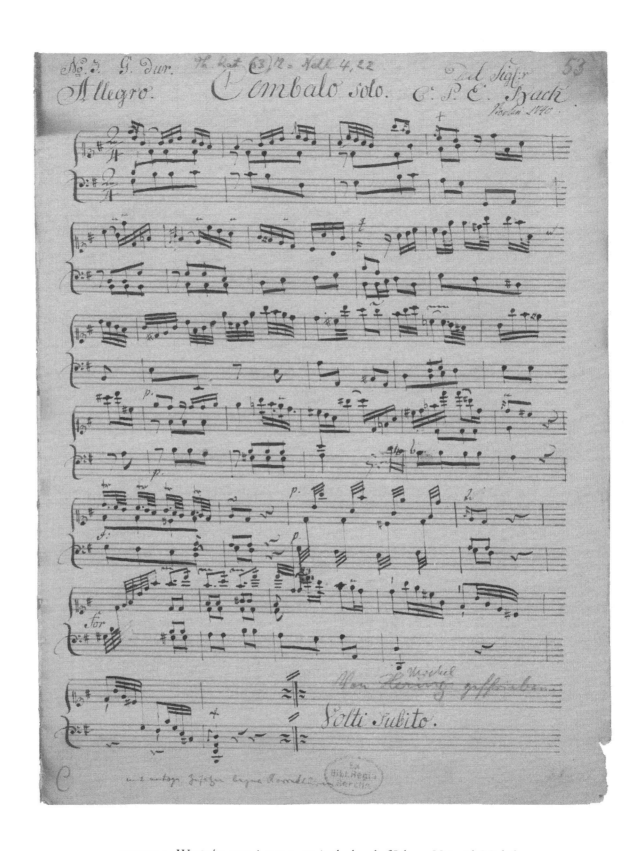

FIGURE 4. Wq 65/12, mvt. i, mm. 1–28, in the hand of Johann Heinrich Michel.
Staatsbibliothek zu Berlin—Preußischer Kulturbesitz,
Musikabteilung mit Mendelssohn-Archiv, Mus. ms. Bach P 772, p. 53

Sonata in G Major

Wq 65/12

Sonata in B Minor

Wq 65/13

Molto adagio

Allegro molto

Sonata in D Major

Wq 65/14

194

FIGURE 5. Title page of Haffner's *Oeuvres mêlées, Partie I.*
Washington, Library of Congress, M23 .O3 (Case)

Sonata in D Minor

Wq 62/4

Sonata in E Major

Wq 62/5

Andantino

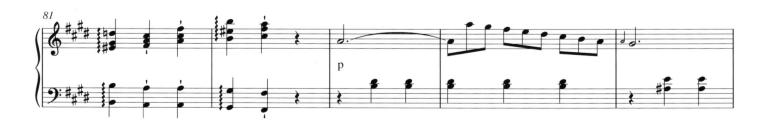

CONCORDANCES

The following three tables provide concordances of three catalogues of C. P. E. Bach's keyboard sonatas. The last column indicates where each sonata is published in the edition *Carl Philipp Emanuel Bach: The Complete Works*.

H	Helm, E. Eugene. *Thematic Catalogue of the Works of Carl Philipp Emanuel Bach.* New Haven: Yale University Press, 1989.
NV 1790	*Verzeichniß des musikalischen Nachlasses des verstorbenen Capellmeisters Carl Philipp Emanuel Bach.* Hamburg, 1790.
Wq	Wotquenne, Alfred. *Thematisches Verzeichnis der Werke von Carl Philipp Emanuel Bach.* Leipzig: Breitkopf & Härtel, 1905.

Concordance of Wq and H Nos. by NV 1790 Numbering

No. in NV 1790	Wq No.	Helm No.	CPEB:CW
1	62/1	2	I/5.1
2	65/1	3	I/6.1
3	65/2	4	I/6.1
4	65/3	5	I/6.1
6	64/1	7	I/6.1
7	64/2	8	I/6.1
8	64/3	9	I/6.1
9	64/4	10	I/6.1
10	64/5	11	I/6.1
11	64/6	12	I/6.1
13	65/5	13	I/6.2
14	65/6	15	I/6.2
15	65/7	16	I/6.2
16	65/8	17	I/6.2
17	65/9	18	I/6.2
18	65/10	19	I/6.2
19	62/2	20	I/5.1
20	65/11	21	I/6.2
21	62/3	22	I/5.1
22	65/12	23	I/6.2
32	65/13	32.5	I/6.2
36	65/14	42	I/6.2
37	62/4	38	I/5.1
38	62/5	39	I/5.1
39	62/7	41	I/5.1
40	62/6	40	I/5.1
42	65/15	43	I/6.3
45	65/16	46	I/6.3
46	65/17	47	I/6.3
47	65/18	48	I/6.3
48	65/19	49	I/6.5
49	65/20	51	I/6.3
51	69	53	I/6.3
52	65/21	52	I/6.3
54	65/22	56	I/6.3
55	62/8	55	I/5.1
56	65/23	57	I/6.3
57	62/9	58	I/5.1
58	65/24	60	I/6.3
59	65/25	61	I/6.3
60	62/10	59	I/5.1

No. in NV 1790	Wq No.	Helm No.	CPEB:CW
62	62/11	63	I/5.1
63	65/26	64	I/6.4
66	62/13	67	I/5.1
67	65/27	68	I/6.4
75	62/14	77	I/5.1
76	65/28	78	I/6.4
81	65/29	83	I/6.4
86	65/30	106	I/6.4
89	62/15	105	I/5.1
91	62/16	116	I/5.1
92	65/31	121	I/6.4
93	62/18	118	I/5.1
94	62/19	119	I/5.1
95	62/17	117	I/5.1
96	62/20	120	I/5.1
98	62/22	132	I/5.1
100	65/32	135	I/5.1
101	62/21	131	I/5.1
114	65/33	143	I/6.4
118	65/34	152	I/6.4
128	65/37	174	I/6.4
130	65/38	175	I/6.4
131	65/39	176	I/6.4
132	65/40	177	I/6.5
133	65/41	178	I/6.5
147	65/42	189	I/6.5
148	65/43	192	I/6.5
151	65/44	211	I/6.5
152	65/45	212	I/6.5
155	65/46	213	I/6.5
157	60	209	I/5.1
159	62/23	210	I/5.1
167	62/24	240	I/5.1
174	65/47	248	I/6.5
195	65/48	280	I/6.5
205	65/49	298	I/6.5
206	65/50	299	I/6.5

Concordance of NV 1790 and H Nos.
by Wq Numbering

Wq No.	No. in NV 1790	Helm No.	CPEB:CW
60	157	209	I/5.1
62/1	1	2	I/5.1
62/10	60	59	I/5.1
62/11	62	63	I/5.1
62/13	66	67	I/5.1
62/14	75	77	I/5.1
62/15	89	105	I/5.1
62/16	91	116	I/5.1
62/17	95	117	I/5.1
62/18	93	118	I/5.1
62/19	94	119	I/5.1
62/2	19	20	I/5.1
62/20	96	120	I/5.1
62/21	101	131	I/5.1
62/22	98	132	I/5.1
62/23	159	210	I/5.1
62/24	167	240	I/5.1
62/3	21	22	I/5.1
62/4	37	38	I/5.1
62/5	38	39	I/5.1
62/6	40	40	I/5.1
62/7	39	41	I/5.1
62/8	55	55	I/5.1
62/9	57	58	I/5.1
64/1	6	7	I/6.1
64/2	7	8	I/6.1
64/3	8	9	I/6.1
64/4	9	10	I/6.1
64/5	10	11	I/6.1
64/6	11	12	I/6.1
65/1	2	3	I/6.1
65/10	18	19	I/6.2
65/11	20	21	I/6.2
65/12	22	23	I/6.2
65/13	32	32.5	I/6.2
65/14	36	42	I/6.2
65/15	42	43	I/6.3
65/16	45	46	I/6.3
65/17	46	47	I/6.3
65/18	47	48	I/6.3
65/19	48	49	I/6.5
65/2	3	4	I/6.1
65/20	49	51	I/6.3
65/21	52	52	I/6.3
65/22	54	56	I/6.3
65/23	56	57	I/6.3
65/24	58	60	I/6.3
65/25	59	61	I/6.3
65/26	63	64	I/6.4
65/27	67	68	I/6.4
65/28	76	78	I/6.4
65/29	81	83	I/6.4
65/3	4	5	I/6.1
65/30	86	106	I/6.4
65/31	92	121	I/6.4
65/32	100	135	I/5.1
65/33	114	143	I/6.4
65/34	118	152	I/6.4
65/37	128	174	I/6.4
65/38	130	175	I/6.4
65/39	131	176	I/6.4
65/40	132	177	I/6.5
65/41	133	178	I/6.5
65/42	147	189	I/6.5
65/43	148	192	I/6.5
65/44	151	211	I/6.5
65/45	152	212	I/6.5
65/46	155	213	I/6.5
65/47	174	248	I/6.5
65/48	195	280	I/6.5
65/49	205	298	I/6.5
65/5	13	13	I/6.2
65/50	206	299	I/6.5
65/6	14	15	I/6.2
65/7	15	16	I/6.2
65/8	16	17	I/6.2
65/9	17	18	I/6.2
69	51	53	I/6.3

Concordance of NV 1790 and Wq Nos. by H Numbering

Helm No.	No. in NV 1790	Wq No.	CPEB:CW
2	1	62/1	I/5.1
3	2	65/1	I/6.1
4	3	65/2	I/6.1
5	4	65/3	I/6.1
7	6	64/1	I/6.1
8	7	64/2	I/6.1
9	8	64/3	I/6.1
10	9	64/4	I/6.1
11	10	64/5	I/6.1
12	11	64/6	I/6.1
13	13	65/5	I/6.2
15	14	65/6	I/6.2
16	15	65/7	I/6.2
17	16	65/8	I/6.2
18	17	65/9	I/6.2
19	18	65/10	I/6.2
20	19	62/2	I/5.1
21	20	65/11	I/6.2
22	21	62/3	I/5.1
23	22	65/12	I/6.2
32.5	32	65/13	I/6.2
38	37	62/4	I/5.1
39	38	62/5	I/5.1
40	40	62/6	I/5.1
41	39	62/7	I/5.1
42	36	65/14	I/6.2
43	42	65/15	I/6.3
46	45	65/16	I/6.3
47	46	65/17	I/6.3
48	47	65/18	I/6.3
49	48	65/19	I/6.5
51	49	65/20	I/6.3
52	52	65/21	I/6.3
53	51	69	I/6.3
55	55	62/8	I/5.1
56	54	65/22	I/6.3
57	56	65/23	I/6.3
58	57	62/9	I/5.1
59	60	62/10	I/5.1
60	58	65/24	I/6.3
61	59	65/25	I/6.3
63	62	62/11	I/5.1
64	63	65/26	I/6.4
67	66	62/13	I/5.1
68	67	65/27	I/6.4
77	75	62/14	I/5.1
78	76	65/28	I/6.4
83	81	65/29	I/6.4
105	89	62/15	I/5.1
106	86	65/30	I/6.4
116	91	62/16	I/5.1
117	95	62/17	I/5.1
118	93	62/18	I/5.1
119	94	62/19	I/5.1
120	96	62/20	I/5.1
121	92	65/31	I/6.4
131	101	62/21	I/5.1
132	98	62/22	I/5.1
135	100	65/32	I/5.1
143	114	65/33	I/6.4
152	118	65/34	I/6.4
174	128	65/37	I/6.4
175	130	65/38	I/6.4
176	131	65/39	I/6.4
177	132	65/40	I/6.5
178	133	65/41	I/6.5
189	147	65/42	I/6.5
192	148	65/43	I/6.5
209	157	60	I/5.1
210	159	62/23	I/5.1
211	151	65/44	I/6.5
212	152	65/45	I/6.5
213	155	65/46	I/6.5
240	167	62/24	I/5.1
248	174	65/47	I/6.5
280	195	65/48	I/6.5
298	205	65/49	I/6.5
299	206	65/50	I/6.5

Made in the USA
Middletown, DE
22 March 2021